Beaver Ed's
Beaver Tales
Word Game
WORDPLAY
6
W9-BMY-194
The
Book
of

WORDPLAY 6

INSTRUCTIONS:

Beaver Ed's Beaver Tales is the silliest, funniest, happiest, craziest, most awesome word game you'll ever play.

Just follow these simple directions:

Before every story in this book, you'll find four columns of words, each marked with a symbol.

Each symbol represents the following:

Symbol

Noun

Verb

Adjective

Wacky words

In each story, you'll find blank spaces marked with any one of the symbols above. Fill in each blank space with a word from that column until all the blank spaces in the story are filled. Finally, read your Beaver Tales aloud to see what kind of wacky, silly, hilarious story you've created.

Change the words and you'll have a different story every time!

WORDPLAY 6

REVIEW

Just so you know:

A NOUN

is the name of a person, place or thing.

Teacher, park, ear, and bus are **nouns.**

A VERB

is an action word.

Fly, run, throw, and bite are **verbs.**

An ADJECTIVE

describes something or somebody.

Fat, tall, cute, round, and thick are **adjectives.**

A WACKY WORD

is any word that will make the story wackier.

Strange Animal

Nouns

Elf
Chipmunk
Gargoyle
Leprechaun
Tiger
Camel
Giraffe
Bear
Toilet
Chicken
Hippo
Fairy

Adjectives

Fuzzy
Fat
Wacky
Weird
Angry
Unhappy
Chubby
Crazy
Thin
Jittery
Stinky
Lucky

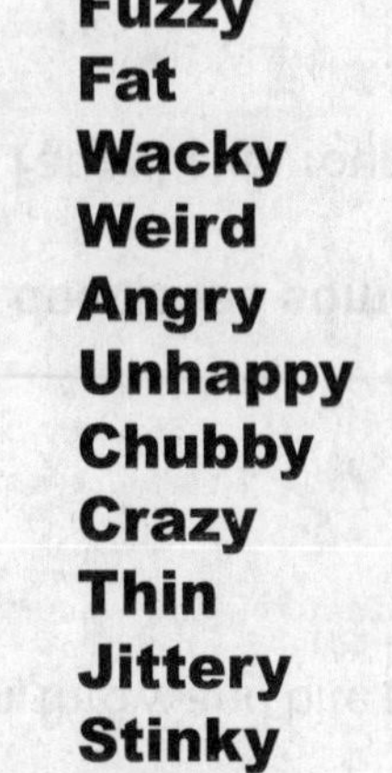

Hey Kids... Use the words on this page or make up your own words for each story.

Verbs

Bark
Crow
Burp
Yodel
Shriek
Screech
Squeal
Giggle
Growl
Snarl
Howl
Roar

Wacky Words

Fulee
Fancypants
Nosy
Nosypicker
Dingy
Dingbat
DroopyLips
Diddledum
Wormy
Grungy
Giggly
Smirkyface

Strange Animal

Mister ________________ was always known as a/an ________________ man.

Not because he lived with a/an ________________, and not because he married a/an

________________ ________________, but because he had a pet

________________. He called him ________________ ________________.

And it wasn't like other pets you may have seen before. This one had the head of a/an

________________, the body of a/an ________________ and the legs of a

________________ ________________. And it didn't ________________ like

you would imagine. Instead, it would ________________ really loud day and night.

And that made all the neighbors ________________ and ________________.

There was so much noise I had to wear special earplugs made out of ________________

________________ hair.

Best-Selling Books According To The Wall Street Gerbil

NOUNS

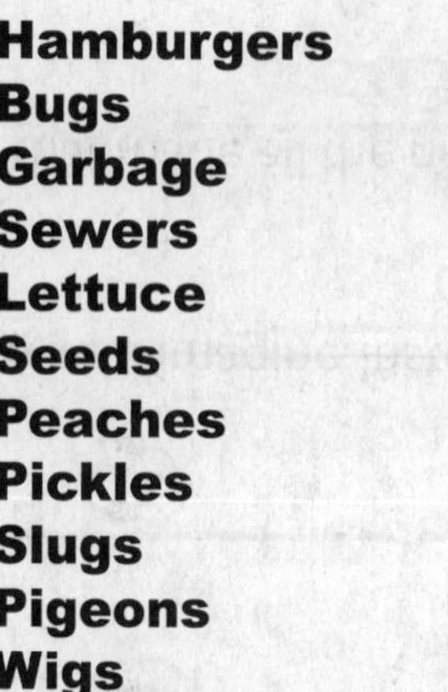

Hamburgers
Bugs
Garbage
Sewers
Lettuce
Seeds
Peaches
Pickles
Slugs
Pigeons
Wigs
Shrubs

ADJECTIVES

Jumpy
Evil
Nefarious
Despicable
Ambitious
Smart
Crazy
Cool
Tasty
Ruthless
Pushy
Stinking

Hey Kids... Use the words on this page or make up your own words for each story.

VERBS

Sing
Shriek
Screech
Squeal
Giggle
Chomp
Scamper
Howl
Roar
Nibble
Gnaw

WACKY WORDS

ChubbyCheeks
HairyHead
Squirrelly Eyes
BuckTeeth
Acornbreath
TreeDweller
Fraidypants
NoTalent
HoleDigger
NutEater
CedarNose
BigBuzz

Best-Selling Books According To The Wall Street Gerbil

1. ______________ and ______________ : Not just for rats anymore.

By Chef ______________

2. The life and times of Dirk ______________ : ______________ Gerbil wrestler.

A/an ______________ autobiography.

3. The forests I have known by Chunky ______________

4. Avoiding ______________ racoons: A users guide.

By T.Bag

5. How to fight ______________ ______________ and live to tell about it.

By Punchy ______________

6. 101 ways to eat ______________ bugs.

By Chew Moore

A Day In The Park

NOUNS

Swing
Rattlesnake
Banker
Orangutan
Frog
Newt
Puppy
Acrobat
King
Clown
Astronaut
Ferret

ADJECTIVES

Ferocious
Dangerous
Silly
Prickly
Bumpy
Poisonous
Hairy
Cranky
Frizzy
Muddy
Dirty
Loopy

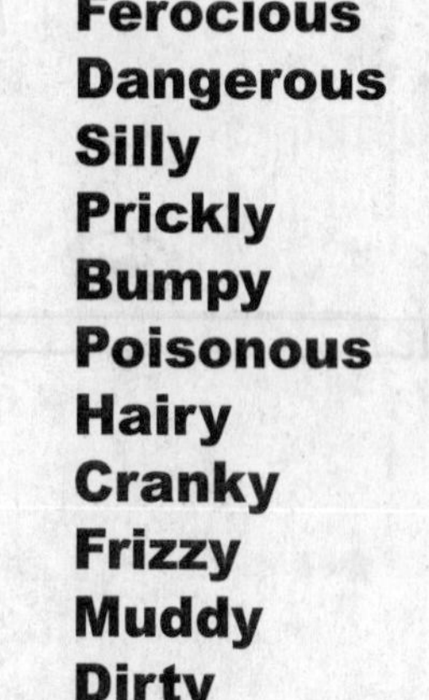

Hey Kids... Use the words on this page or make up your own words for each story.

VERBS

Bark
Crow
Burp
Yodel
Shriek
Screech
Squeal
Giggle
Growl
Snarl
Howl
Roar

WACKY WORDS

Dingerhopper
Frubble
Nosy
Nosypicker
Dingy
Dingbat
DroopyLips
Diddledum
Wormy
Grungy
Giggly
Smirkyface

A Day In The Park

Today, my best friend Martha ____________, her brother, Mr. ____________ and I headed out on our annual hike through the ____________ National Park. The region was known for it's ____________ ____________ (s) that had lived there since the early 1900's. You never really did get to see them, but you could always hear them ____________ in the woods. Sometimes, we would ____________ back just to let them know they weren't alone. My Mom told me of a/an ____________ tale about one of them venturing into the city looking for fresh ____________. The ____________ County Police had to ____________ really loud to scare them back into the woods.

Picture Perfect

Nouns

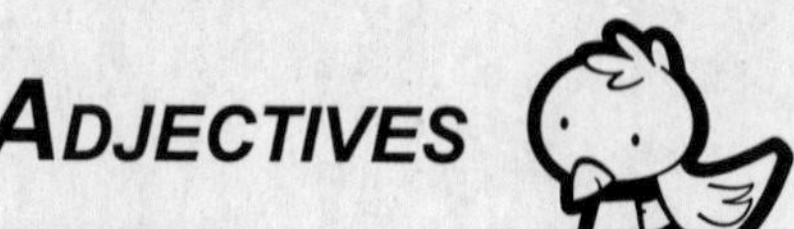

Adjectives

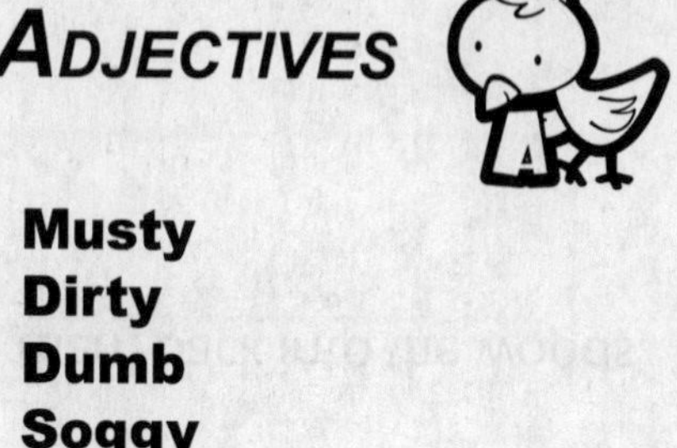

Nouns	Adjectives
Porcupine	Musty
Caterpillar	Dirty
Warthog	Dumb
Oyster	Soggy
Monkey	Wet
Crocodile	Dreadful
Beaver	Sweaty
Centipede	Clammy
Bee	Damp
Teabag	Awful
Hippopotamus	Outrageous
Gorilla	Stupid

Hey Kids... Use the words on this page or make up your own words for each story.

Verbs

Wacky Words

Verbs	Wacky Words
Scream	Bignose
Spit	Badbreath
Yodel	Wigglebutt
Burp	Dogface
Whistle	Burp Queen
Puke	DinkyDip
Vomit	Le Pignose
Gag	Zitface
Heave	Ogreyes
Groan	Lizard tongue
Whine	Nowzpicker
Whimper	Teenybrain

Picture Perfect

Ugh! Getting my picture taken for the ______________ school yearbook was about as much fun as having someone ______________ in your ear, but it had to be done. I could tell Cathy ______________ was excited because she wore a/an ______________ new dress. She even put ______________ -flavored gloss on her big lips to make them ______________ and shiny. Gross! I didn't even bother to comb my ______________ hair. My teacher, Mr. ______________ said it looked like I had a giant ______________ on my head. When it was my turn, I sat in the ______________ chair and smiled. Then, just when the photographer took the picture, I decided to ______________ . Now that's a picture I'll remember for a long time!

Rock Star

Nouns

Porcupine
Caterpillar
Warthog
Oyster
Monkey
Crocodile
Beaver
Centipede
Bee
Teabag
Hippopotamus
Gorilla

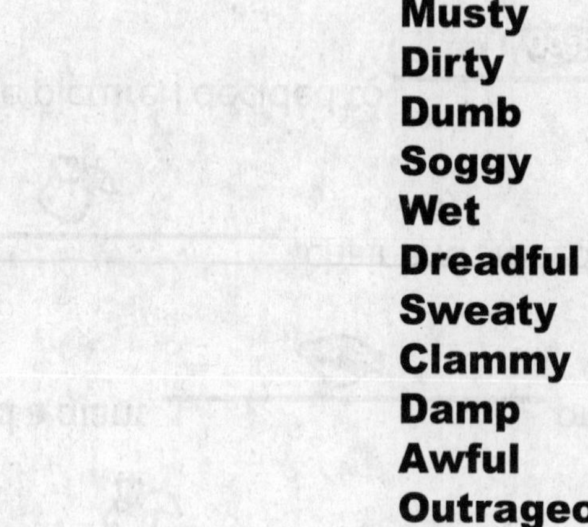

Adjectives

Musty
Dirty
Dumb
Soggy
Wet
Dreadful
Sweaty
Clammy
Damp
Awful
Outrageous
Stupid

Hey Kids... Use the words on this page or make up your own words for each story.

Verbs

Scream
Spit
Yodel
Burp
Whistle
Puke
Vomit
Gag
Heave
Groan
Whine
Whimper

Wacky Words

BusButt
Picklenose
Doofus
Airhead
Mollycoddle
Kerfuffle
Wheezerhopper
Sockbreath
Blubberlips
EvilEye
Goonygoat
Dribble Cheeks

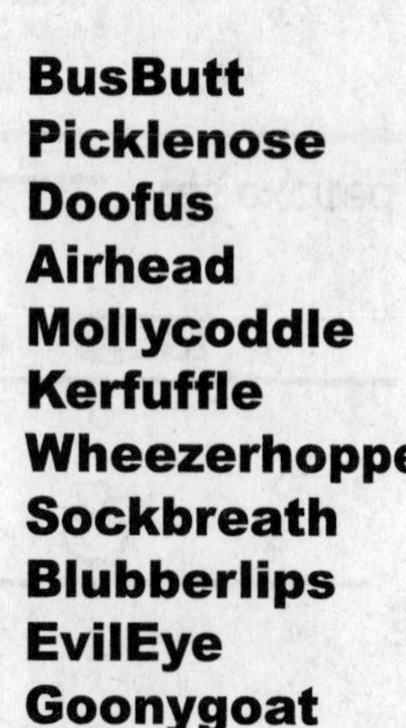

Rock Star

Jimmy ____________ was the coolest teenager in the whole world. He was so cool girls would ____________ every time he walked by them. He looked like a cross between a really ____________ ____________ and a very handsome ____________. He sang in a band called Doctor ____________ and the ____________ ____________. They had two ____________ songs on the local radio station. The first was called "I ____________ every time I see your ____________ face" and the second song was an even more popular one called "I really, really love you ____________. Do I sound like I'm jealous? No way!

Dumb Nursery Rhymes

Nouns

Berry
Baboon
Balloon
Prune
Tune
Fly
Soap
Tie
Dad
Mom
Sewer
Sweater

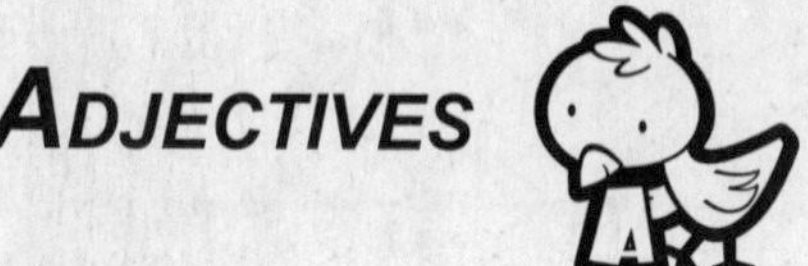

Adjectives

Fat
Green
Purple
Chubby
Skinny
Dead
Round
Flabby
Bad
Mean
Crazy
Dumb

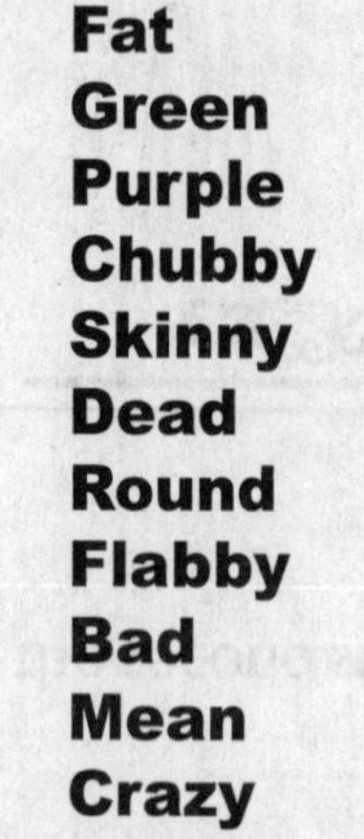

Hey Kids... Use the words on this page or make up your own words for each story.

Verbs

Stumbled
Danced
Tripped
Fell
Slipped
Tumbled
Cried
Puked
Frowned
Screamed
Wheezed
Gasped

Wacky Words

Woofy
Wazzy
DingDong
Dingle
MangyMutt
Chinnychinchin
Flabbygut
ChubbyChub
Taterface
BoxButt
Nozehare
Patootie

Dumb Nursery Rhymes

Even though you'll never see these ________________ nursery rhymes in a library,

they are still fun to read.

Baa Baa Black ________________

Baa baa,

________________ Sheep, Have you any ________________ (s) ?

Yes sir, yes sir, Three ________________ bags full.

One for my ________________ , One for my ________________ ,

And one for the ________________ girl That lives in the lane!

Hey diddle diddle

Hey diddle diddle, The ________________ and the fiddle, The cow ________________

over the ________________ .

The little dog ________________ to see such sport,

And the ________________ ran away with the ________________ .

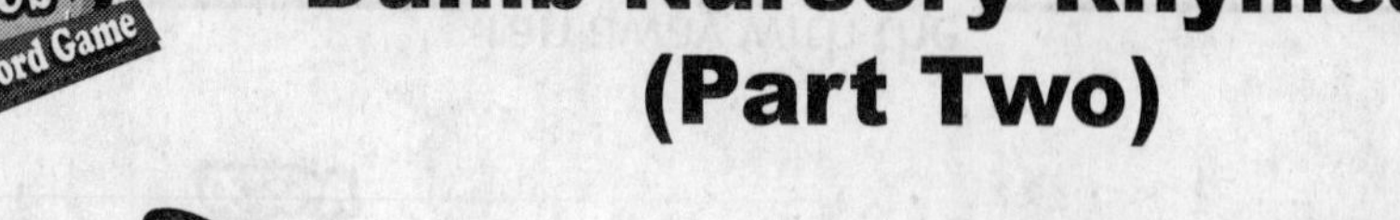

Dumb Nursery Rhymes (Part Two)

Nouns

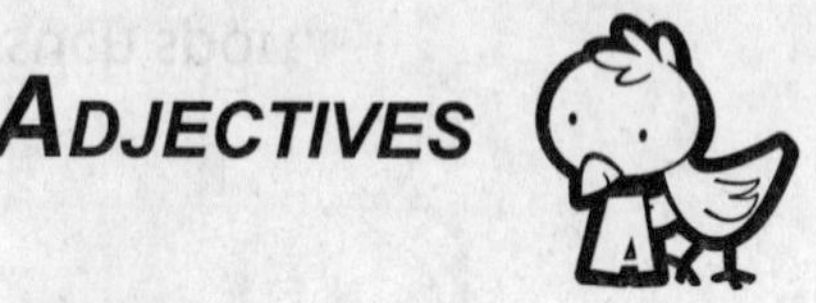

Adjectives

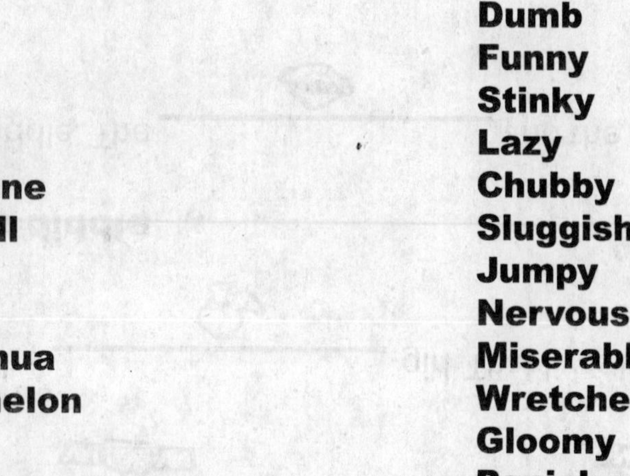

Nouns	Adjectives
Donut	Dumb
Toilet	Funny
Cat	Stinky
Diaper	Lazy
Porcupine	Chubby
Meatball	Sluggish
Dwarf	Jumpy
Ferret	Nervous
Chihuahua	Miserable
Watermelon	Wretched
Clown	Gloomy
Unicorn	Panicky

Hey Kids... Use the words on this page or make up your own words for each story.

Verbs

Wacky Words

Verbs	Wacky Words
Stumbled	Mushymush
Danced	Gunk
Tripped	Glop
Fell	Gloop
Slipped	Goo
Tumbled	Slime
Cried	Yuckysoup
Puked	Slop
Frowned	Muck
Screamed	Ploop
Wheezed	WeaselJuice
Gasped	WeeWee

Dumb Nursery Rhymes (Part Two)

I don't know why this is, but little ________________(s) love nursery rhymes,

especially the ________________ ________________ ones. Sometimes, I like to

change the words around. That makes the ________________ (s) a little bit more

________________.

JACK BE ________________

Jack be ________________ Jack be ________________

Jack ________________ over the candlestick. ________________ be nimble.

________________ be quick. Someone get me a/an ________________ quick!

LITTLE MISS MUFFET

Little Miss Muffet Sat on a ________________

Eating her ________________ and whey Along came a ________________ ,

That sat down beside her And ________________ Miss Muffet away.

Old Man Johnson

Nouns

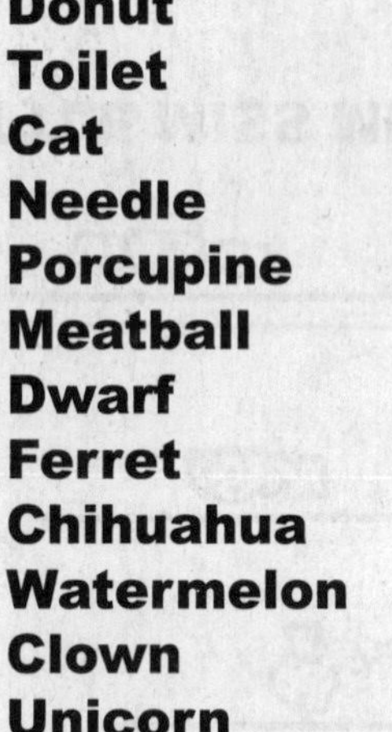

Donut
Toilet
Cat
Needle
Porcupine
Meatball
Dwarf
Ferret
Chihuahua
Watermelon
Clown
Unicorn

Adjectives

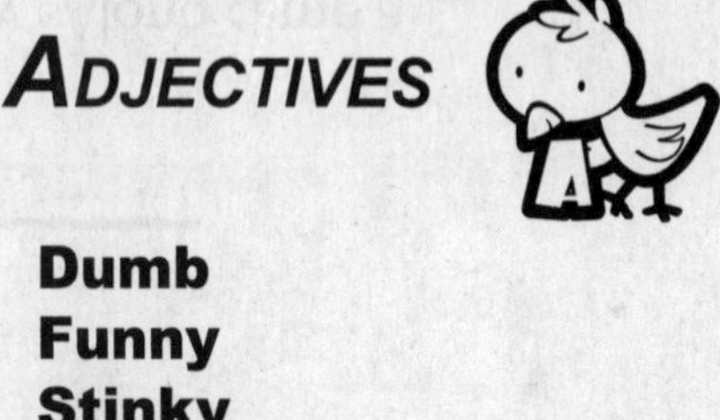

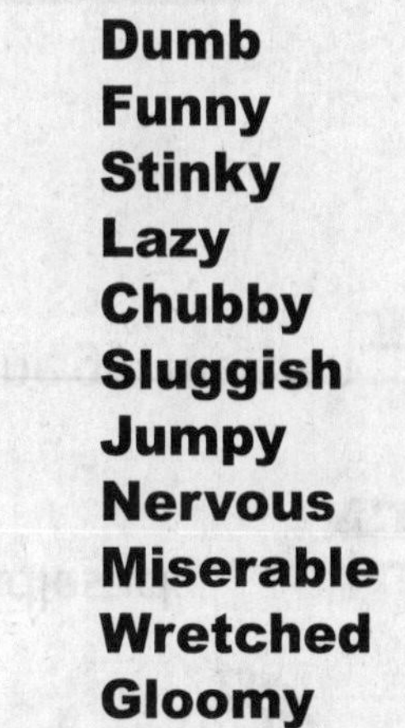

Dumb
Funny
Stinky
Lazy
Chubby
Sluggish
Jumpy
Nervous
Miserable
Wretched
Gloomy
Panicky

Hey Kids... Use the words on this page or make up your own words for each story.

Verbs

Scream
Whisper
Ruin
Damage
Burp
Destroy
Spoil
Punch
Kiss
Kick
Squeeze
Lick

Wacky Words

Mushymush
Gunk
Glop
Gloop
Goo
Slime
Yuckysoup
Slop
Muck
Ploop
WeaselJuice
WeeWee

Old Man Johnson

Every time I sing this ________________ song, the people around me ____________ .

If we sing it together, you can ________________ too?

Old Man Johnson had a ________________ , H-E-L-L-O.

And on his ________________ he had a cow, H-E-L-L-O.

With a ________________ here and a ________________ there,

Here a moo, there a ________________ , everywhere a ________________ .

Old Man Johnson had a ________________ , H-E-L-L-O.

And on his ________________ he had a pig, H-E-L-L-O.

With an ________________ here and an ________________ there,

Here an oink, there a ________________ , everywhere a ________________ .

Old Man Johnson had a ________________ , H-E-L-L-O.

Happily Ever After

NOUNS

Fairy
Mannequin
Tree
Brick
Sandal
Purse
Box
Gerbil
Toaster
Toad
Robot
Tomato

ADJECTIVES

Stupid
Mushy
Awful
Unbelievable
Amazing
Farfetched
Unlikely
Boring
Ridiculous
Ludicrous
Foolish
Exciting

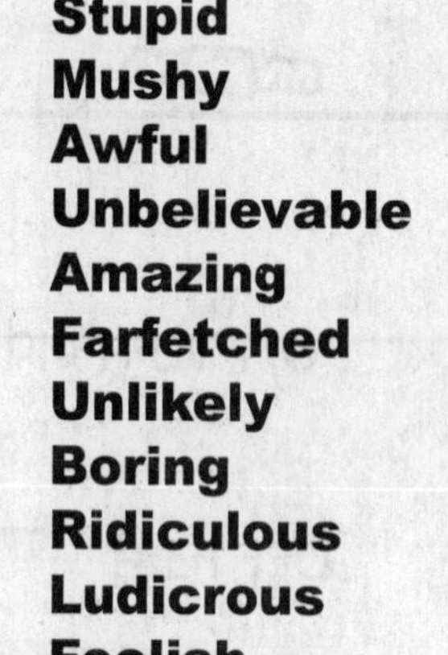

Hey Kids... Use the words on this page or make up your own words for each story.

VERBS

Talk
Walk
Burp
Eat
Nap
Snooze
Bathe
Clean
Paint
Fart
Belch
Blink

WACKY WORDS

DumbTown
MuckVille
SpitCity
New York Spitty
Spilladelphia
Smellifornia
Borelando
Disturbia
Grease
Pooston
Spittsburgh
Rhodent Island

Happily Ever After

I know this story is going to sound ________________ but it's true. Not too long ago, in a place called ________________ there was a/an ________________ man who married a ________________ ________________ . Honest to goodness! The townsfolk said it was wrong, but he didn't care, he was in love. On his wedding day he invited all of his ________________ friends and ________________ family but no one came. They said they had to ________________ that day and couldn't make it. But he knew they were just ________________ . Sadly, they moved into a big ________________ in ________________ , opened a ________________ factory and together they lived happily ever after.

Riding Rules

NOUNS

Gnome
Piano
Monkey
Spoon
Beanie
Goose
Potato
Pimento
Flower
Cookie
Torpedo
Baseball

ADJECTIVES

Wet
Idiotic
Fuzzy
Ugly
Smelly
Heavy
Damp
Soggy
Soft
Stupid
Boring
Filthy

Hey Kids... Use the words on this page or make up your own words for each story.

VERBS

Sing
Scream
Shake
Eat
Ignore
Burp
Belch
Forget
Change
Grab
Photograph
Mix

WACKY WORDS

Red
Yellow
Green
Blue
Black
White
Gold
Orange
Purple
Brown
Gray

Riding Rules

Before you go bike riding, it is important to ________________ all the safety rules.

After all, you wouldn't want to be on your ________________ and crash into a/an

________________ ________________ . First, before sitting on your

________________ , make sure you have a ________________ ________________

on your head and a ________________ ________________ on your ________________ .

And don't forget to look both ways before you ________________ the

________________ . And always remember to use the ________________

________________ when you change lanes. If you ________________ these rules,

you'll always have a ________________ time riding your ________________ .

Best-Selling Books For Kids

NOUNS

Butter
Batter
Comb
Cat
Shoe
Sock
Finger
Cork
Watch
Vegetable
Potato
Foot

ADJECTIVES

Dead
Rubber
Burnt
Smelly
Slimy
Loopy
Moldy
Artificial
Poison
Bad
Stupid
Boring

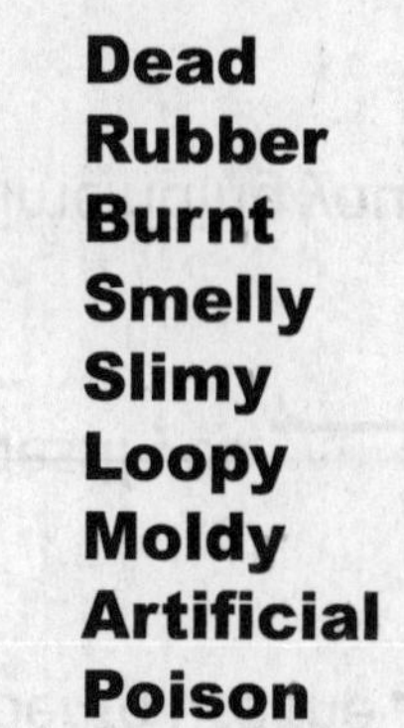

Hey Kids... Use the words on this page or make up your own words for each story.

VERBS

Lick
Belch
Squeeze
Bite
Cook
Pluck
Squash
Kiss
Sniff
Bathe
Slap
Punch

WACKY WORDS

Cowpie
Piggie
Iggy
Mimi
BugEyes
BaggyPants
Zitface
BigNose
Blabbermouth
Thingamajig
Whatchamacallit
PlumberBoy

Best-Selling Books For Kids

I love books! Just thinking about all the __________ stories makes me want to __________ a librarian. These are some of my favorites:

1. __________ Potter and the Sorcerer's Stone

2. __________ eggs and ham

3. Charlotte's __________

4. How the __________ stole Christmas

5. One Fish. Two Fish, Red Fish, __________ Fish

6. Charlie and the __________ factory.

7. __________ you forever.

8. Nancy Drew's __________ stories

9. Are you there, God? It's me __________

10. To __________ a Mockinbird

A Commercial Break

Nouns

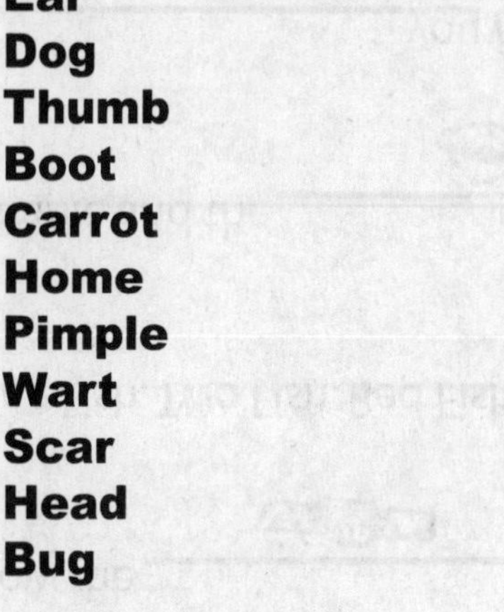

Nose
Ear
Dog
Thumb
Boot
Carrot
Home
Pimple
Wart
Scar
Head
Bug

Adjectives

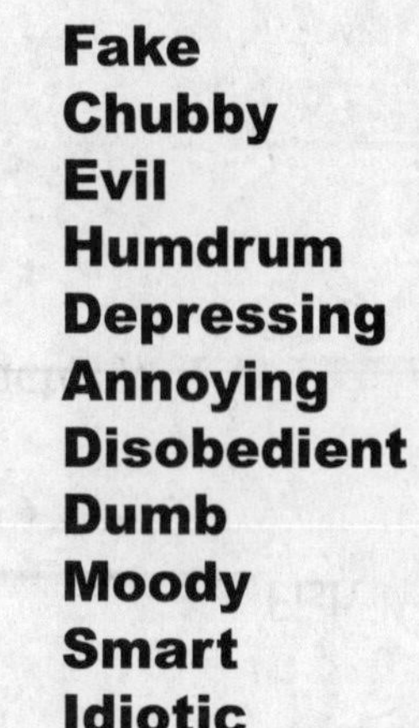

Fake
Chubby
Evil
Humdrum
Depressing
Annoying
Disobedient
Dumb
Moody
Smart
Idiotic
Nice

Hey Kids... Use the words on this page or make up your own words for each story.

Verbs

Breathe
Run
Smirk
Heave
Jump
Holler
Fly
Die
Brush
Snore
Shiver
Shake

Wacky Words

WooWoo Paste
Artificial Strawberry Stuff
Whatchamacallit
Egg cleaner
Blabbermouth
Not-so-Super Thing
Loose Lips
Buzzzzzz meter
Something something!
Not-so-Silly Thing
Thingamajig
Waxy Stuff

A Commercial Break

We interrupt this ________________ episode of Beaver Tales for a/an ________________ message from our sponsor. Are you tired of being called ________________? Are you having trouble with your ________________ ?

Would you like to ________________ like they do in the movies? If you answered yes, then it's time you tried… Super ________________ ! After one week you'll have a thinner ________________ , a bigger ________________ and a more muscular ________________ . ________________ now and we'll throw in a free ________________ just for being so ________________.

Why ________________ when you can ________________ , thanks to this ________________ product! Pick up the phone and ________________ now!

Brought to you by the makers of Silly ________________.

Beaver Ed's Theme Song

Nouns

Adjectives

Nouns	Adjectives
Nose	Fake
Ear	Chubby
Dog	Evil
Face	Dull
Boot	Fuzzy
Hair	Enormous
Home	Mini
Pimple	Dumb
Wart	Moody
Scar	Smart
Hat	Idiotic
Mom	Nice

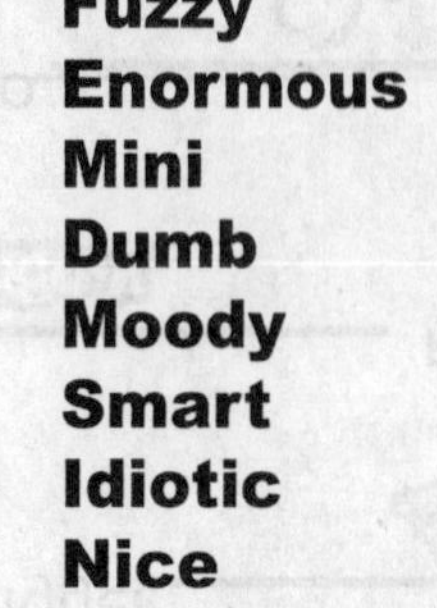

Hey Kids... Use the words on this page or make up your own words for each story.

Verbs

Wacky Words

Verbs	Wacky Words
Hum	Coochie
Yodel	Meezle
Vomit	Goofy
Heave	Adoody
Jump	BugEyes
Holler	Schtinky
Sing	Schmelly
Burp	Noogie
Jiggle	Lurby
Snore	Flinky
Shiver	Loopy
Shake	BaggyPants

Beaver Ed's Theme Song

Beaver Ed, Beaver Ed, my ________________ is wrong.

If your name is ________________ then this is your song.

You can ________________ with your Mom, you can ________________ alone.

It's ________________ either way, so drink some ________________ cologne.

Beaver Ed, Beaver Ed, your ________________ is on fire.

If you are ________________ raise your voice a little higher.

You can ________________ with your Dad, you can ________________ it alone.

It's ________________ either way, so get your ________________ on the phone.

So ________________ it like you mean it, like your ________________ is on TV.

And do a little ________________ for you and for me.

Start The Day Right

Nouns

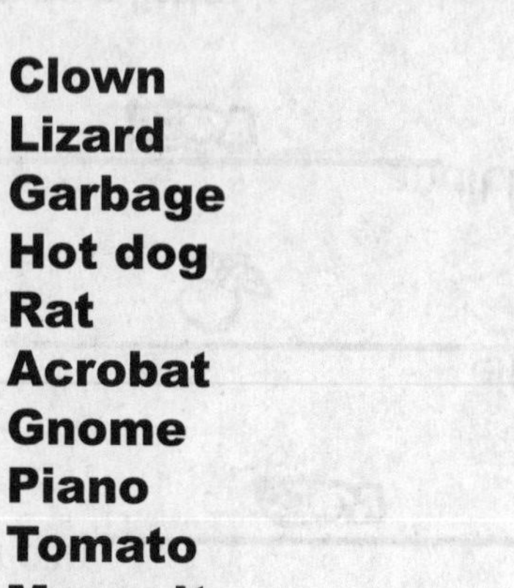

Clown
Lizard
Garbage
Hot dog
Rat
Acrobat
Gnome
Piano
Tomato
Mosquito
Aardvark
Hamster

Adjectives

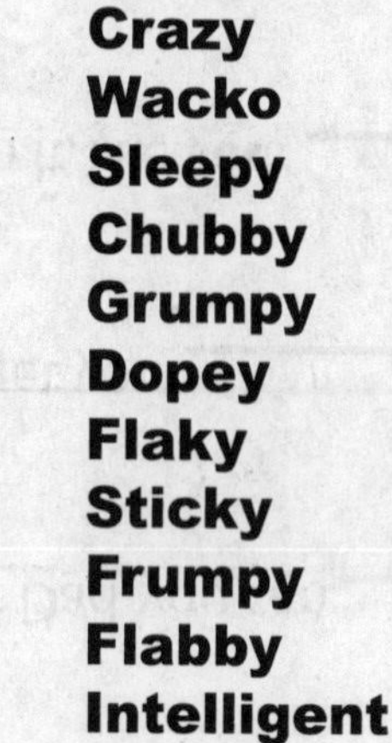

Crazy
Wacko
Sleepy
Chubby
Grumpy
Dopey
Flaky
Sticky
Frumpy
Flabby
Intelligent
Antique

Hey Kids... Use the words on this page or make up your own words for each story.

Verbs

Dance
Spit
Shake
Shiver
Jump
Scream
Throw up
Sing
Whisper
Sleep
Snore
Whistle

Wacky Words

Knishy
Knoshy
KNooshy
Flardy
Furty
Hamook
Karky
Willby
Groosh
Papoopa
Liggy
Diggy

Start The Day Right

There's no doubt about it, breakfast is the most ________________ meal of the day. In my house, it's a ________________ time to fuel up and get your ________________ energized. Studies have shown that a/an ________________ who skips breakfast is more likely to eat ________________ meals for dinner. Some people think a donut and a/an ________________ is a great way to start the day off, but I know you need to eat something with more nutritional value like boiled ________________ , a slice of ________________ ________________ meat or a toasted ________________ . Other great ideas would be a boiled ________________ and baked ________________ with a glass of ________________ juice.

Not In My Backyard

NOUNS

Banana
Gerbil
Bean
Diaper
Gnome
Nail
Toilet
Sock
Mouse
Yeti
Mailman
Egg

ADJECTIVES

Hilarious
Muffled
Unusual
Disgusting
Creepy
Silly
Scary
Loud
Strange
Surprising
Poor
Bizarre

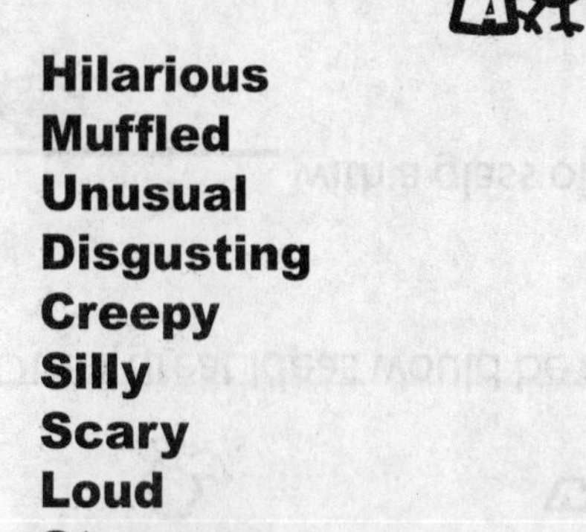

Hey Kids... Use the words on this page or make up your own words for each story.

VERBS

Jiggled
Yodelled
Disintegrated
Doodled
Dawdled
Snored
Choked
Painted
Burped
Tinkled
Waddled
Surfed

WACKY WORDS

Plooper
Burby
Weeny
Nurnee
Schlurp
Kermy
Winky
Swoopy
Flingy
Grunky
Flurby
GooGoo

Not In My Backyard

Yesterday morning, I ________________ after breakfast and went in the backyard to sit by the ________________ . All was quiet when I heard a ________________ ________________ noise coming from my neighbour's ________________ . I slowly ________________ my way over, climbed the ________________ ________________ tree and looked in Mrs. Johnson's prized ________________ garden. To my surprise, I saw a/an ________________ ________________ eating a fresh ________________ . When he saw me, he screamed, "________________!" It frightened me so much my ________________ fell off. I picked it up, turned and went back into my yard. I guess Mrs. ________________ will just have to deal with these things on her own.

My Library

Nouns

Nose
Ear
Dog
Face
Boot
Hair
Home
Pimple
Wart
Scar
Hat
Mom

Adjectives

Fake
Chubby
Evil
Dull
Fuzzy
Enormous
Mini
Dumb
Moody
Smart
Idiotic
Nice

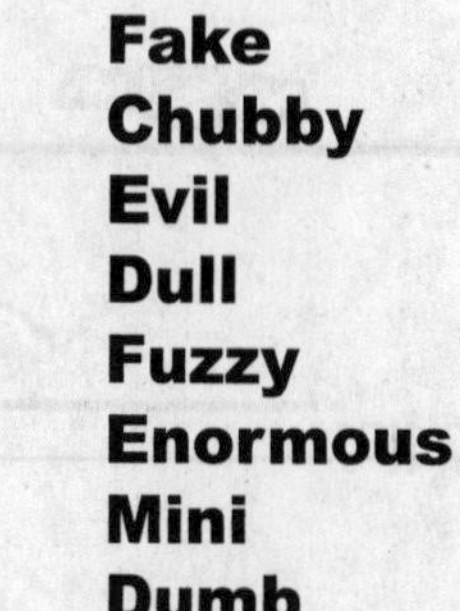

Hey Kids... Use the words on this page or make up your own words for each story.

Verbs

Hum
Yodel
Vomit
Heave
Jump
Holler
Sing
Burp
Jiggle
Snore
Shiver
Shake

Wacky Words

Coochie
Meezle
Goofy
Adoody
BugEyes
Schtinky
Schmelly
Noogie
Lurby
Flinky
Loopy
BaggyPants

My Library

When you're bored, the neighbourhood library is a/an ________________ place for adventure. If you just use your ________________ , you'll find a whole world of ________________ stories and ________________ tales. It doesn't matter what age you are, there is always something ________________ going on.

Just ________________ right in, grab a ________________ book and start to ________________ . You'll find books that can teach you how to make ________________ like a pro, and others that can show you how to be a/an ________________ person. My favourite books are about the legendary ________________ and the ________________ ________________ .

They are always a great read at any age!

UFO Troubles

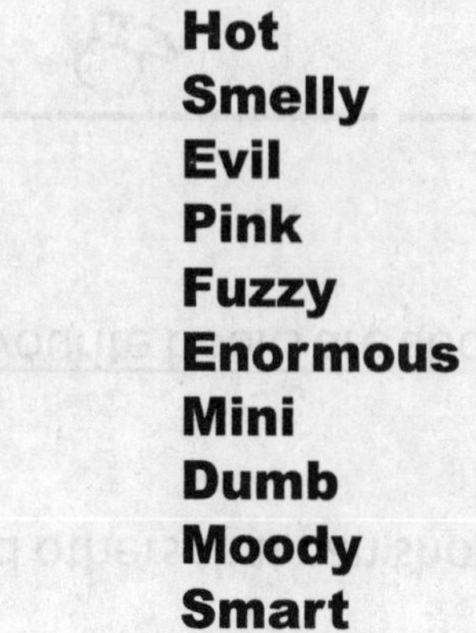

Nouns

Nose
Ear
Dog
Face
Boot
Hair
Granny
Pimple
Wart
Scar
Hat
Mom

Adjectives

Hot
Smelly
Evil
Pink
Fuzzy
Enormous
Mini
Dumb
Moody
Smart
Green
Moldy

Hey Kids... Use the words on this page or make up your own words for each story.

Verbs

Hum
Yodel
Vomit
Heave
Jump
Holler
Sing
Burp
Jiggle
Snore
Shiver
Shake

Wacky Words

Coochie
Meezle
Goofy
Adoody
BugEyes
Schtinky
Schmelly
Noogie
Lurby
Flinky
Loopy
BaggyPants

UFO Troubles

A spaceship just crashed into my ________________ . It is still ________________ from the impact of entering the earth's atmosphere. I couldn't believe the ________________ next door never saw the light flash or heard the ________________ ________________ noise. The aircraft had crushed my ________________ . Part of it was upside down on my neighbour's cat, ________________ .

When the ________________ opened, out stepped a/an ________________ , ________________ alien who looked more like a giant ________________ than a classic space invader. I started ________________ near him and screamed ________________ ! He looked at me with his three ________________ eyes and blurted out ________________ . It was truly love at first sight.

Check out many more great Beaver Tales from Beaver Ed!

- Beaver Ed's Beaver Tales Word Play
- Beaver Ed's Beaver Tales Word Play 2
- Beaver Ed's Beaver Tales Word Play 3
- Beaver Ed's Beaver Tales Across the Country
- Beaver Ed's Beaver Tales Back-to-School
- Beaver Ed's Beaver Tales Fun with People

and many many many more!

check out www.beaverbooks.ca

Color Beaver Ed

Other products from Beaver Books Publishing

"Fun to Learn and Do" Workbooks

- Printing Fun
- I Can Write
- Addition & Subtraction Gr.1-2
- Number Skills K-1
- Activity Fun Book
- Kindergarten Skills
- Multiplication Skills gr. 2-4
- Division Skills gr. 2-4
- Phonics pre K-K
- Phonics K-1
- Fun with Reading K
- Fun with Reading Gr.1
- Fun with Math K
- Fun with Math Gr.1
- Spelling K-1
- Spelling 1-2
- Spelling 2-3
- Math 1
- Math 2
- Math 3

Wipe Clean Products

- Counting Fun 1-25
- I Can Print
- Alphabet Fun
- Colors Shapes Numbers
- Doodle and Write
- Learn to Draw
- Learn to Print
- Learn Your Numbers
- Learn Your ABC's
- Learn to Tell Time
- Learn Your Shapes
- Insect Express – Activity book
- My Days of the week – Activity book
- Catch a Germ – Activity book
- Ocean Games – Activity book
- Addition - JUMBO boards
- Subtraction - JUMBO boards
- Multiplication - JUMBO boards
- Division - JUMBO boards

Puzzles

- Fish Alphabet
- Counting 1- 10
- Know Your Shapes
- Learn Your Colors

Wordboy

- My Sister is a Snake
- My Mommy is a Number
- My Family's Full of Shapes
- My Baby Brother is a Werewolf
- My Grandpa is an Owl

All Products are available in French and Spanish.

Check out Beaver Books online at:

www.beaverbooks.ca